9781923359352
AF600856
BFFS
SWEET!
SQUAD GOALS
BFFS
SWEET!

WOW!
BFF
HELLO

BETTER
TOGETHER

IN
MY
BESTIES
ERA
!!

FRIENDS LIFT ME UP

SO CUTE!

LOL
HELLO
HELLO
BFF
BFF
WOW!
HELLO
HELLO
BFF
HELLO
LOL

DOORABLES

HIGH FIVES!
SQUAD GOALS

READY
FOR
ACTION

HELLO
BFF
WOW!
HELLO
WOW!

WOW!
BFF
WOW!
HELLO
HELLO
SO MANY FRIENDS!
HELLO
LOL
SWEET MOVES!
HELLO
HELLO